Pat...

MOLLY & MAXI

An eight-legged love story

Thank you for
helping us help
other animals

Molly

Maxi

Patricia Danter

MOLLY & MAXI

An eight-legged love story

MEREO
Cirencester

Mereo Books

1A The Wool Market Dyer Street Cirencester Gloucestershire GL7 2PR
An imprint of Memoirs Publishing www.mereobooks.com

Molly and Maxi: 978-1-86151-469-1

First published in Great Britain in 2015
by Mereo Books, an imprint of Memoirs Publishing

The address for Memoirs Publishing Group Limited can be found at
www.memoirspublishing.com

The Memoirs Publishing Group Ltd Reg. No. 7834348

The Memoirs Publishing Group supports both The Forest Stewardship Council® (FSC®) and the
PEFC® leading international forest-certification organisations. Our books carrying both the FSC
label and the PEFC® and are printed on FSC®-certified paper. FSC® is the only
forest-certification scheme supported by the leading environmental organisations including
Greenpeace. Our paper procurement policy can be found at
www.memoirspublishing.com/environment

Typeset in 12/18pt Bembo
by Wiltshire Associates Publisher Services Ltd. Printed and bound in Great Britain by
Printondemand-Worldwide, Peterborough PE2 6XD

ACKNOWLEDGEMENTS

My friends Sue and Ann, who knew Molly so well, often said "You should write a book about her". The years went by and when I looked back on the time I had had with Molly I thought "maybe". So I did. I've so enjoyed putting pen to paper. I sincerely thank you, Sue and Ann.

My friend Gillian has given her time to help me. She has used her computer for many of the tasks. This wouldn't have happened without her. Thank you Gillian.

FOREWORD

If you lived in our town you would need no introduction to Molly. She is well known to many people, for various reasons.

Maxi and I met Molly about eight years ago. It seems like a lifetime. We know her and her little idiosyncrasies very well.

One of the good things about Molly is that she entertains herself. Just take her to a wide open space, a field or the beach, and she's off. It gives you a chance to read a book, talk to people or just daydream, safe in the knowledge that she'll return about two hours later. She'll have explored every nook, cranny and pool and chased anything worth chasing. She may be soaking wet and dirty, but she will have had a wonderful time and be tired enough to go home. The only downside to this is that people who see her alone think she is either lost or abandoned.

My Maxi is a pretty laid back sort of fellow. They complement each other. When we go out together Molly will bark at other dogs if they get too close, because sometimes Maxi isn't too keen on approaching other dogs. If we really have absolutely no idea where Molly is, Maxi will go to find her.

Our Molly is loving, good fun, headstrong and willful. Her energy and outlook on life belies her age. We all love her. I sometimes think if she had been born a cat she would have been long gone by now.

Good luck Molly. I hope you have many more fun-filled years ahead of you.

Sue

ABOUT THE AUTHOR

I was born in Cardiff and went to Gladstone school, then Cardiff High. I sat 'O' levels the first year they were introduced into the education system. I left school interested in maths, art and architecture. I went to work in a drawing office and became a draughtswoman, sitting at a large drawing board. Today we have been superseded by graphic designers and computers.

I was married in 1958 and lived in Porthcawl. Finding the travelling to Cardiff tiring, I decided to find a job in Porthcawl. I started work at Newton Primary School in 1963, when they introduced clerical assistance for primary head teachers. I spent over thirty happy years in Newton. Being with so many children helped me to make up for not having children of my own. The short hours – it was never a full time job – and long holidays meant I could have animals and give them a happy life.

Writing has been an enjoyable surprise, and I hope that many animals may benefit from the sales of my book.

Pat Danter

INTRODUCTION

We've always lived with dogs and cats. Our latest dog came to us from PAWS (Porthcawl Animal Welfare Society). My husband used to say that if we had another dog he'd like an 'Eddie Dog' lookalike, Eddie being the dog in the TV series 'Frasier'. One day as he was passing the charity shop belonging to PAWS, my husband saw a picture of an 'Eddie Dog' in the window. He asked if we could see her. He went on his own, as I would have brought home all the little shaggy ones. He was excited when he saw her; just what he was looking for.

PAWS checked our home and garden and said we could have her. They chipped her while we held her, and her vaccinations were up to date. They gave us a logbook with her details and we left the kennels for home. Molly had arrived. She was prettier than Eddie, but little did we know what a character she would be. She is our fifth dog.

The greatest thing in life is to be needed.
Add what you can to life.

OUR FIRST DOG - DANDY

My boyfriend gave me a Pomeranian puppy for my 21st
birthday. He was gorgeous (the dog!) like a pretty, tiny fox
cub. My boyfriend became my husband and we had Dandy
for eight years. Sadly he died of a severe infection.

**There is no greater invitation to love
than in loving first.**

My sister Wendy with Dandy.   Two photographs
of Dandy.

OUR SECOND DOG – FLOSSY

Flossy was meant to be ours. The day we told the vet we wanted a dog that was small and shaggy, he said one had come in that day which was in a bad way, but it had to remain in the kennels a week before we could have her. Flossy was in a terrible state. She couldn't walk because her coat was so long and matted – it was about six inches beyond her feet.

Our first job was to cut off her coat. Underneath was a skinny but pretty grey and white Tibetan terrier-type lookalike.

The vet advised us not to let Flossy off the lead for about six weeks, as she would probably run away. On release day we took her to the beach, thinking she would be safer. She immediately ran away from the beach as fast as she could. We had to go home, get the car, then set out to try to find her. We found her a few miles away, by now running slowly and not really knowing where she was going. It was heartbreaking to see her. It took two years of hard work before Flossy trusted us and became a happy dog. We had her eleven years before she died of kidney failure.

While we had Flossy, our milk lady, Jane, knocked on

our door one day. A dog had followed her milk van all day in the rain. What should she do, she asked? We took him in and dried and fed him. We thought we'd keep him, but Flossy had different ideas. She went on hunger strike after a few days.

We enlisted the help of the vet, who thought he could rehome the dog with a family whose dog had just died. They lived nearby. They fell for the stray that Flossy didn't want to share us with. He became a well-known character, as he never wanted to be in the house but was always out

Flossy's adoption certificate.

and about in the town. There was even a photograph of him standing on the promenade wall on the front of the *Glamorgan Gazette* saying he was a well-known character in the town. Following a milk float in the rain certainly changed his life.

Flossy: I don't need a great deal of love but I do need a steady supply.

Stray: What appears to be the end may really be a new beginning.

Flossy's first day in our garden. She couldn't stand or walk easily, so we just sat her down.

Flossy with my father at Rest Bay, minus her matted coat,
so skinny – what a difference!

Flossy years later, very happy sitting with next door's cat.

OUR THIRD DOG - SMOKEY

A picture of a pretty, shaggy dog, held in the arms of a kennel maid, appeared on the front page of the Gazette. He was described as a shaggy mongrel with a little bit of standard poodle in him.

We went to see him; he looked so old and frail. He had been found wandering the streets, and was thought to be blind with very bad arthritis. We said we'd take him home and give him lots of cuddles, warmth and food. The kennels said we'd probably only have him a week or two.

We named him 'Smokey', as he was grey and so slow. Over the weeks we discovered that he wasn't blind but deaf. His sight was poor, but he knew where he was going in the house and garden. When you came up behind him he would jump, which was what led us to think he was deaf.

When going to bed he would turn round and round, as dogs do when they are lying down, but poor Smokey had to be helped because of his arthritis. We gave him as good as life as possible with his handicaps. His sight also deteriorated.

When we were out with him one day around the duck pond he saw a quick movement out of the corner of his eye, and before I could stop him he fell into the pond. He started swimming away from the bank, and being old I knew he couldn't swim for long. No use shouting, he couldn't hear me. Only one thing for it – go in and fetch him out. The cold water had really perked him up, and he walked home with a spring in his step, while I felt embarrassed with my wet clothes clinging to me. Luckily we didn't meet anyone.

He finally lost his sight and life became more and more difficult. Sadly we had to have him put to sleep. He had been a lovely pet needing a lot of care, which made us love him more. We had him for an amazing eighteen months.

The greatest thing in life is to be needed.

**No act of kindness, no matter how small,
is ever wasted.**

Smokey

The story about
Smokey on the
front of the
Glamorgan Gazette

HIS coat isn't much to look at, and his eyes have clouded over with cataract. They are not sure about his parentage, but he would appear to have a little bit of standard poodle in him.

The dog is a shaggy mongrel which has been at the Canine League's kennels for over a month ever since he was found wandering by the roadside, either lost or abandoned.

It is a great shame, because he is a friendly little dog, who is taking his present circumstances stoically. He will be kept by Mr. Jack Price and his staff at the kennels until "something turns up."

The shaggy mongrel is being well cared for by the two kennel maids, Susie Spriggs and Geraldine Francis.

The kennel staff hope good homes can be found for the dogs in their care. They don't want to find them accommodation and then get the same animals returning a couple of months later.

No dog is destroyed; they are all kept until homes are found for them.

If you have lost a dog, give the kennels a ring on Bridgend 2771. If you want a dog, why not go along and see if there is one that takes your fancy?

● Kennel maid, Susie Spriggs comforts the lo mongrel "with a bit of standard poodle in hir who has been a tenant at the Tondu Road kenn for over a month.

OUR FOURTH DOG – TESS

Our lovely Tess, who sadly didn't see her first birthday.

A young, pretty, black long-haired mongrel with a white front, Tess came to us because a friend was worried that she was not happy with a member of his family. He already had a boxer and had got Tess from a dog's home for company for the boxer, but as he was working they had very little exercise. Tess was only five months old. Our friend knew she was the sort of dog we liked: medium size, shaggy and pretty. We fell for her and she came to live with us.

We failed to find out if she had had her vaccinations. We thought that as she came from a dogs' home she would be covered. Unfortunately that summer there was an outbreak of distemper in our town; Tess succumbed, and she was not covered. We and the vet tried to save her, in vain. This happened in the early 1970s, when vaccinations and communication were not as good as they are today.

Tess sadly died, not quite a year old. This was the saddest thing that happened to us and our dogs.

Tomorrow is not promised us, so let us take today and make the most of it.

OUR FIRST CAT - SOLOMON

A rest from dogs was enforced on us by a stray cat falling in love with the cat next door, who was a boy, and castrated. We had no idea who his owner was; there were no notices up anywhere about a lost cat. We asked at PAWS – no luck.

Our stray spent more and more time following the cat next door everywhere. I felt sorry for him and started feeding him. He slowly wormed his way into our home and our affections, and we adopted him.

He wasn't castrated and got into a few fights. One day one of his puncture wounds from fighting went septic and we took him to the vet. We had to name him on the spot. We called him 'Solly', short for Solomon. We thought he was a very wise cat moving in with us.

The vet suggested that to avoid fighting that we should have Solly castrated. His wound healed, and we discussed the forthcoming operation. He went out at night and slept in during the day.

One night he didn't return. We spent a lot of time looking for him around our area. The police, vet and the dogs' home were contacted, but there was no sign of Solly. We think he knew the meaning of the word 'castration'. He was with us less than six months, which was too short.

Small streams of caring become a pool of love

Solly – what a handsome boy he was!

OUR SECOND CAT - POPPY

Neighbours had heard that our cat had gone missing, and one of them was putting food out for hedgehogs in his garden. A cat started visiting and eating the food. Other neighbours had seen it sleeping in the sunshine in people's gardens. It didn't seem to have a home.

Then the neighbour who was feeding the hedgehogs called at our house one day. Would we have the cat? They already had a dog, and the wife didn't like cats.

Hello cat! It was Armistice Day, so we named her 'Poppy'. She didn't seem very well and was sick a lot after eating. She must have eaten everything she could find when she hadn't had a proper home.

I have live yogurt for breakfast each day, and after a lot of stomach problems it helped, so I began giving it to Poppy. She loved it and after five or six weeks she wasn't ill any more. When Molly came I thought to do the same for her, and she had live yogurt every day after coming to us. Poppy spent eleven years with us and was very happy and contented.

She had an inoperable growth deep in her ear; I do not think that she knew it was there as there were no symptoms. Slowly, over the years, it took her sight.

She was wonderful; she managed to get to her favourite place – the summer house – for over a year. This involved negotiating three small sets of steps, then going through a door and on to her chair in the warm sunshine.

We had to be careful that we left everything in the same place. Finally, when life got too much for her, we had her put to sleep.

Three pictures of Poppy. She always found the suitcase as soon as it appeared.

Small streams of caring become a pool of love

All these animals came into my life before Molly. As you can see, I have had plenty of experience with animals. However I had no inclination to write a book about them – until Molly came into our lives.

Real love begins where nothing is expected in return.

MOLLY'S STORY

I would like to tell you all about my life. It's been so interesting, thanks to the people who love me. I can't remember dates, just events in my life. My owner has put comments in brackets.

This is the first picture of Molly. She has climbed up on the settee and followed every mouthful of our breakfast. .

I am a girl dog *(a mad terrier)*. My first owner couldn't manage me, and didn't seem to know where I was from one moment to the next. I learned that if I brought my ball back to her and placed it on her feet, she would throw it again. If I walked alongside her I used to rub against her legs so she knew where I was. I would stand between her legs when she stopped to talk to other people, so she didn't have to worry where I was.

Sadly she put me up for homing. *(The owner lost her eyesight, making it impossible for her to keep Molly, as it would have been too dangerous. She could have fallen over Molly, who was three years old and very active.)*

I went to live in kennels, where I felt very sad. Although I had lots of other dogs for company, I didn't like many of them. I wanted to go home to my owner. The people who looked after me tried to cheer me up, but I lost my fur and got skinny. So skinny that they thought I needed worming, but I was just sad.

One day after being kennels for four months a nice man came to see me. I'm sure he liked me because he took me home *(December 16th 2005)*.

How lucky am I? I have a new mum and dad, a new home and a lovely big lawn to play on. I sleep in a comfy bed downstairs. M and D (Mum and Dad) sleep upstairs. They give me lovely food – M calls it 'supper'. I eat it fast, so I am putting on weight and I think my fur is growing.

Molly swimming for the first time.

I don't feel so cold when I go out now, although M insists I wear a coat. I hate it and just go stiff and can't move. It's a bit cissyish. I'm a girl, but I am also a terrier.

I live by the sea, and M and D take me down to the beach and play ball. There's water there, I'm not sure why, but it seems to disappear sometimes.

They also take me round the duck pond, where there are lots of ducks and a pair of swans. There's a lovely field

3

Top picture, the field in which Molly and Maxi
first saw each other.

next to the duck pond, it's become my favourite place. We
were there one day, about six months after I had arrived at
my new home. M and D were in the bushes picking
blackberries when this beautiful, black curly dog appeared.
It was love at first sight for both of us, and we played and
played. His name is Max, his owner is Sue. We have been
inseparable since, what fun!

We visit our field often, and we see rabbits – I chase
them but do not catch them. We've seen lots of pretty
butterflies, a heron, and I've smelt a fox (M saw it). I like
rolling in the anthills, but M doesn't like it as I go brown
and am covered in ants. *(I have to get them off her.)*

Since meeting Maxi my life has been wonderful,
though there is the odd hiccup. Sometimes M and D seem

to disappear *(holidays)* and they take me to stay where there are lots of dogs. It reminds me of the place I went to before M and D gave me a home. There were lots of noisy dogs there, so I joined in. I did wonder if I had to stay there for a long time. They fed me and I had my comfy bed, but I missed M and D. It wasn't long before they came to fetch me and I was back in my comfy house and lovely garden. I love M and D. I realised that when I thought I wouldn't see them again.

You can see why she fell for him - isn't he handsome?

Playing happily in their field.

Another hiccup in my lovely life I don't quite understand. They take me to a funny-smelling place *(the vet)*. There are dogs and cats there, and none of them seem to like it. We go into another room and they try to lift me on to a table, I'm not having that! They gather around me on the floor, and I'm right by the door hoping to escape as soon as possible. They usually stick a needle in me, which I don't like. I don't know what it's for *(vaccinations)*. I'm really glad to get out from there. I do make a fuss, I don't know why, I can't help it.

I have lots of fun on the beach. Maxi likes to go in the water, but it looks very cold to me. I like playing with the ball and sticks. If children are playing football on the beach I like to join in. I'm good at dribbling with my nose and I make people laugh. M has taught me to push the ball between her legs and she shouts "goal!" and everybody laughs again.

I play a lot of football in the garden, on the lawn. I do hear M saying it looks more like a field than a lawn. It's not quite so green, but browner. I get brown as well, and it's still fun. M and D chase me around the garden and pour water over me to get me white again, then we have fun with the towels. The best bit is lovely warm air coming from a noisy thing *(the hairdryer)*.

Talking about noise, quite suddenly there comes a night when there are lots of bangs after it gets dark *(fireworks)*. This has happened so many times while I have been living by the water. I bark and bark so much and run as fast as I can, wherever I can. When it's over I am so thirsty, but I can't get my breath so I lie and pant until I feel a bit better, then I have a long drink of water. It takes me a long time to settle down as I keep listening for the bangs and then I will have to start all over again barking and running - I can't help it.

I've found a new game. When we go down to the beach digging holes I'm still not sure about the water, even though Maxi loves it. If I dig the sand near the water when the hole gets bigger there is some water in the bottom so my feet get wet. I like that, it's cool, but still not like the water Maxi goes into that keeps moving and making a noise. After digging lots of holes I think I like water.

I run up and down at the edge of the water chasing balls and sticks. The most fun I have is banging all the bubbles on the edge of the water with my nose - they seem to come out of the sand so I pop them, good fun.

One very hot summer's day we were on Newton beach, and Maxi was already in the water when M joined him. She started calling me, so I slowly walked into the water to go to her. I tried to reach her but she didn't seem to be getting any nearer *(I was slowly moving backwards)* when suddenly I wasn't walking and my feet weren't on the ground – I was swimming. It felt natural and I enjoyed it. M and Sue were making a lot of noise *(we were cheering her)*. I came out and shook myself. Wow it felt good! And I was cool on such a hot day. *(From that day to this Molly*

has been unable to keep from water of any kind - her distant
ancestors must have had webbed feet and fins!)

So far in my life my favourite places have been the field
and the beaches. One day, when it was very sunny, we went
in Sue's car. Maxi and I sat in the back, M and Sue in the
front. A short journey later we arrived at a car park with
grass all round. Out we all got and enjoyed the grass on
the dunes. We eventually came to water *(Kenfig Pool)* –
wow, lots of lovely still water. We had lots of company, lots
of dogs running around and in the water chasing balls and
sticks, lots of people and children were sitting around too.
We went to this lovely place often on sunny days. This is
definitely my favourite place now, what fun.

Molly with Sue

One day while playing and swimming in Kenfig Pool I saw something moving in the water *(fish)*. I ran after them jumping and swimming. I couldn't catch them but I wagged and wagged my tail. Since then I've spent years chasing them. I haven't caught any, but I've nearly wagged my tail off trying.

(Molly has become quite a character at Kenfig Pool; so many people ask us what she is doing. Many people remark what a wonderful time they have had watching her. She's been photographed and filmed by people. It does warm your heart to watch her jumping out of the water, swimming and wagging her tail so much while she is looking in the water for those elusive fish.)

Molly at home in her garden.

Molly turning our lawn into a field.

I don't know what they are doing in the garden. My green lawn (well, it's mostly brown mud now) is being dug up and being put in something that has been built by D in the middle of the garden *(a raised bed)*. Now there are strange men here they've put down a hard green lawn, not fussed with it *(chippings)* and smooth stones around the edge *(paving stones)*. I now have good fun running and running around the edge like a race track *(Molly treats it like Silverstone)* and I can still play football and stay clean. D has also put a step against the garden wall. I can stand on this and watch the children playing next door. I like children, they are fun. *(We think there were children in Molly's life with her previous owner. When she first came to us she looked expectant and excited when she saw a pushchair and would pull towards it.)*

I am very lucky that I used to have two walks a day, one with D in the morning and one with M in the afternoon. Now D has had a bad leg and doesn't take me for a walk so often. I sometimes go with Maxi and Sue along the prom in the morning, then almost every afternoon. M takes me with Sue and Maxi on lovely long walks. On the way home we pass a house where cats live. One of them, a little black cat called Toffee, is very old and small. I don't think she is very well, so I sniff her and I wouldn't think of chasing her. M loves to stop and smooth her. She rubs her head in M's hand and puts her little tongue out. I think she is saying "I like that". We see her lots of days, I think she waits for us, she knows the time like I do. I know exactly when it's time for my food, my walk, my chew and my milk.

(Summer holidays are here.) Today I've had a lovely day. Porthcawl is very noisy with lots of funny smells and people everywhere. The four of us are on the front beach enjoying ourselves when children with nets and buckets join us. I'm so excited they are throwing the ball for me and I'm running everywhere. I start digging a hole in the sand; the children thought it was great and they were laughing, then they started putting water in my hole. They kept filling it up and I kept digging, what fun! I am shattered, you wouldn't recognize me, I am sand coloured.

(November 11th) Today I don't know why I haven't been

We are tired and 'bonding'.

taken for a walk. It's very wet and noisy outside (*we've had severe weather, thunder and lightning*). All day long M and D have played with me, but it's not the same as a walk. It hasn't happened before, and I hope it won't happen again as I have so many beans to use up.

(*November 17th*) Today I've had a lovely walk and splashed in the pools on the beach. Coming home I suddenly smelt a lovely smell. I took off under some railings into the trees and bushes; I was very busy for a long time following the smell around. I had fun. (*Near the sand dunes is a wooded area surrounded by railings. Many dog walkers had said they had seen foxes in this area. Molly was racing around and was in there about half an hour covering herself with as much fox excrement as she could find. What a pong!*)

Having a rest before the fun starts again.

The fun ended when I got home and M put me in the bath and scrubbed me until all the nice smell had gone. I must say I still smelled nice after I was dried, but a different nice, I preferred the first one.

(November 21ˢᵗ) We've had a lovely walk today over the sand dunes with Sue and Maxi. A husky dog followed us, we had seen her earlier running around on her own. She came to us and lay on her back. M put her on my lead, Sue put Maxi and me on one lead and we walked along together with the lead between us. The dog took us all

home to where she lived, then she knocked on a flap with her nose and two little boys said that she was their dog and took her in – it was different!

(January 4ᵗʰ 2013) It's a little cold for the pools, so I do not stay in long. I can climb up a slope from the beach to a house guarded by big dogs. I run around and they follow me, barking. It's good fun. I found a way in today – the dogs like me, the big, big furry one sits and watches me, the other big black one runs around with me. I bark at the little dogs inside looking out of the glass doors. *(I am very cross with Molly for doing this as it is private property. These dogs, a Pyrenean Mountain Dog and a Rottweiler, are guard dogs, so I thought. However, the Pyrenean sat and watched her and the Rottweiler wagged his tail and wanted to play, but they could have killed her and it would have been my fault. I shouted at her in a very stern voice and out she came.)*

(16ᵗʰ January) I couldn't resist leaving M, Sue and Maxi in the bowl and going to see the dogs. It was a long way, but I found them. They were pleased to see me, and to add to the fun there was a cat in the garden. I chased the cat and she ended up on the top of the caravan. I jumped and jumped but I couldn't reach her. I went inside and tried to jump up to the ceiling to get the cat, but failed. M eventually dragged me back through the fence with the help of Sue. Fun for me.

(1ˢᵗ February) I've been taken to that funny-smelling

place again. They put me on the table, shaved me, and did something to both my back and front leg. I was so glad to come home.

(Molly had had a lump on her back leg for about twelve months, but it had hardened and we made a decision to have it removed before she went climbing rocks in the summer and could knock it. We had aspirations done on the lump and unfortunately it turned out to be a nasty aggressive tumour).

(8th February) In that funny smelling place again, lots of talking and we leave. We get in the car and guess what? We end up in another funny-smelling place. M and D leave me. I'm in a strange place with lots of people and noise, and then I go to sleep. I wake up still in a strange world. M and D come and take me home – hooray! I am very uncomfortable and my legs are funny. I am in my bed downstairs and M has stayed with me all night. The only good thing is that I am eating lovely food – chicken, rice and chicken stock. *(Molly had her tumour removed today with some leg muscle. The good news was that the surgeon removed it complete.)*

(13th February) I had a lovely night last night back in my bedroom, in my bed and on my own. I spent two nights in my bed downstairs with M on the settee and two nights in my bed in their bedroom. I know I've been crying a lot as my routine has been messed up this last week, I haven't had any decent walks and I haven't seen Maxi. Sue has

been a few times and I tell her all about what is going on. *(We laugh as Molly chunters away when Sue comes. It sounds as though she is telling her about her operation.)*

(22ⁿᵈ February) I'm in that funny-smelling place again, I don't know why, a lady cuts something with scissors *(stitches)*. I don't feel a thing. We weren't there long I'm glad to say. I'm home and happy now.

(24ᵗʰ February) Happy day, Sue and Maxi joined us for our walk today. I have missed them but I did feel tired when I got home. I had supper and a lovely long sleep. I am enjoying life again, back to walking, playing, sleeping and having lovely treats from Mum – what fun!

(31ˢᵗ March) Enjoyed my day, but I do not feel like playing with my toys and I don't want my chew.

(1ˢᵗ April) I have been sick, sick and sick all night. M and D have been helping me but I feel so ill. I've been drinking lots of water but it's just coming back up. I've been ill all day and M and D have stayed up with me. I think they are worried about me. I've had a little meal *(chicken and rice)* but I still feel sick. I'm not drinking any more.

(2ⁿᵈ April) I'm being taken in the car to that funny-smelling place again. A nice man has felt me all over and stuck needles in me. I'm back home and all I want to do is sleep, sleep, sleep. M and D have been making me drink nice water *(chicken stock)*. I'm having quite nice liquid

squirted into my mouth with my pills. *(There is a bad diarrhoea and sickness bug about, lots of dogs have had it).*

(3rd April) Today I am hungry and feel a little better, but I don't feel like going for a walk. I miss seeing Sue and Maxi.

(4th April) I've had a little walk, but not with Sue and Maxi.

(5th April) I've had a longer walk today, feeling better but no Maxi. *(Maxi has the same illness and has been as sick as Molly, poor thing.)*

(10th April) All back together again, feeling good.

(13th April) In the car and I'm shaking – where am I going? *(Poor Molly, all her car trips this year have been to the vet.)* I'm in a nice house and garden with one of my favourite playmates. *(My sister and brother-in-law have been wintering in Spain. My brother-in-law plays games with Molly.)* I've had a fun day. I think I smelled a cat, but I haven't found it. It's been such a long time since I saw my playmate.

(18th April) Something is going on in one of my fields *(there's a circus in town).* I'm on the lead, I wish I wasn't. I can smell lovely smells *(circus animals: camels, llamas, pony zebras etc.)* Then I saw something little move *(chickens)* and I wanted to chase and catch them *(I am glad Molly was on the lead, they wouldn't have survived!)*

(19th April) I like being warmer. The sun is shining and

Happy swans and cygnets on our duck pond

I am in the garden in the evening watching and listening to what is going on around me.

(21ˢᵗ April) We were walking around one of my best places – the duck pond - then in to the wood. I could hear lots of birds' wings flapping and flapping, making lots of noise. I went to have a look. There were so many ducks making so much noise that I just jumped in the pond and swam around to see what was up. *(people were feeding bread to the ducks.)* Suddenly a big white duck *(swan)* came towards me so fast. He stood on me and pushed me under

the water. I was scared, I came up barking *(shrieking is a better word!)* He pushed me under three times before I got away. I swam as fast as I could to where M was on the bank with Sue and Maxi. I climbed out, shaking, I definitely used up one of my lives today.

(28th April) I have been in my pools on the beach for the first time this year. I didn't stay long, it was cold, but fun.

(30th April) Today has been a day I have been waiting for. My pools were warm enough for me to spend lots and

Cooling off in the pools

lots of time having fun digging, jumping and wagging my tail. What fun.

(5th May) I am back in that funny smelling place again. I feel very ill and I'm crying a lot with pain. M and D have taken me there and back in the car. I've had needles in my neck. I do not want to eat or drink. I just want to lie down but I can't keep still with the pain. *(Molly had another bout of diarrhoea, she was very poorly).*

(7th May) Today I feel a little better. M is giving me liquid and pills and I've had nice food *(chicken, rice and stock)*. I am hungry, but I am feeling better and going for little walks. It's nice to see Sue and Maxi again.

(24th May) Can you believe it, I'm back in that smelly place again? They put me on the table, I hate it, did my best to get down but a nice young man did lots of things to my eyes. They gave me a treat but I don't like them, then home I came, thank goodness.

(3rd June) Went to meet Maxi and Sue as usual, and guess what, we all got in the car. It's a long time since I'd been in Sue's car *(nearly a year)* but I knew where we were going, my favourite place *(Kenfig Pool)*. Maxi and I took off straight away down to the water, it was lovely and we had hours of fun. As usual I didn't want to come out, but Sue sounded really cross when she shouted my name, so I came out of the pool. Home for supper and I haven't moved since.

(4th June. I have decided to trim Molly's coat today, it's warm

Digging holes.

Is that a fish?

and she's looking scruffy. Her hair is growing well where she was shaved for her surgery so I've balanced it up and she looks better.)

(9th June) Lots of days in the sunshine and lots of days enjoying the pools. Maxi is enjoying the sea. I am so happy.

(17th June) We've walked a long way today, but it was worth it. The weather was hot and Maxi and I were panting, so it was heaven when we got into the water *(Newton beach).* We didn't want to come out to go home.

(18th June) We've done the same again today in the lovely sunshine. How lucky we are to live by the sea, I'm now a water baby. I love it!

(19th June) Another lovely day, keeping my paws crossed we'll be in the sea again. Yea, here we are, what fun! M has bought a bubble gun on the way home, I know the shape! Had to have fun chasing the bubbles before I collapsed. I was so tired after a fab day.

(23rd June) Where has that lovely warm sunshine gone? I don't think I'll get up, I'm going to stay in bed, in the warm. I can see the weather from where I lie in bed, it's rubbish.

(5th July) I've had a wonderful day. I've been in lots of pools and in the sea *(Newton Beach).* I found a lovely hole for digging in. *(Two children had made a lovely castle in the sand and dug a big hole in the middle.)* They laughed and laughed at me. I covered myself in sand from digging as fast as I could, what fun.

Even Molly gives in sometimes.

(6ᵗʰ July) Today life is wonderful. I'm in Kenfig Pool jumping and running looking for fish. I am getting interruptions - lots of dogs are running past me and jumping over me, one pushed me right under the water I barked, and ran at him. He didn't care - he was enjoying himself, like me.

(7ᵗʰ July) Back in Kenfig Pool with Sue and Maxi enjoying the sunshine and the water. Loads of dogs and children, but I'm very busy looking for fish. I do see them and jump at them, but they just disappear.

(12ᵗʰ July) M and D are up early and have gone in the car, I know not where. *(I had a trip to Maastricht for three days with a friend to see Andre Rieu, It was wonderful. I do not think Molly missed me too much, that's a terrier for you).* I don't mind it's hot out there and I'm enjoying the cool in my cool bed. D came back without M and he seems to be in charge. He's feeding me and he is doing good!

(13ᵗʰ July) No sign of M. I hope she is coming back soon. I miss her but I have D, Sue and Maxi. D has gone out in the car in the dark. Where has he gone? The car is

Happy in the sunshine.

Eating ice cream.

Happy together.

In her bedroom.

back and I can hear M's voice. Wow she's back, how lovely! I have missed her a little bit.

(18ᵗʰ July) It's so hot, too hot for Maxi. He doesn't want to go out at all. I don't mind as long as I can go in the pools. We did the pools in the evening and it was lovely.

(19ᵗʰ – 22ⁿᵈ July) It's been so hot, Maxi and I have been so lucky, we've had four wonderful days at Kenfig Pool. I could stay all day it's so lovely but we have to go home to eat and sleep, or do we? I could stay here forever.

(24ᵗʰ July) I've found some really deep rock pools I have to swim in, they're so deep, they're keeping me cool. I'm cooling off in this very hot weather.

(4ᵗʰ August) I'm not getting up too early today, I can hear the rain. As soon as we started our walk it rained cats

Two pictures of Molly keeping an eye on her territory.

Happy dogs at Kenfig Pool with Molly and
Maxi in the background.

and dogs. I'm soaked, M is soaked lots of bangs *(thunder and
lightning)*. Now I'm home in the bath being showered. It's
nice and warm. I saw something move in the bath and I'm
looking for it *(she saw her reflection in the chrome around the
plug hole)*. I'm trying to get down the plughole to catch
what's there. *(I lift her out and she jumps back in, normally she
can't get out quickly enough)*. I've been taken out of the bath
and dried. I've had my supper and I'm content.

(6ᵗʰ August) Today one of my favourite people has come
to see us *(my sister)*. She has come with a little person,
Libby. We played in the rocks and the pools, had fun, then
ice cream, lucky me.

Molly with Ann, one of her favourite people

17-year-old Toffee. Molly doesn't chase her,
just sniffs her bottom.

(12th August) It's a lovely day and I feel full of beans. I'm in my usual pools, but I feel very adventurous. I'm off right across the front beach, it's all rocks and pools and my tail won't stop wagging. I know M will be waiting for me *(two hours)* when I've finished my adventure.

(13th August) I feel full of beans again today. We're on the little beach in front of the lighthouse and I've had a lovely time in the sea jumping the waves with Maxi and chasing stuff in the sea *(seaweed)*.

(14th August) Today I'm rock climbing, jumping over rocks and looking in pools. I've really used up my beans well this week.

(18th August) I'm having a real terrier day today. We're in the field. Maxi has a new toy and is very busy, so I've toddled off into the long grass and bushes. Wow! Lots of lovely smells. I'm getting a bit smelly and very wet, what fun. I've been in here a long time, so I'd better go and see where M, Sue and Maxi are. There they are, here I come. They are shouting to me to go away and won't let me sit by them. I'm trying hard, it's fun. *(She is black and stinks.)*

Home, I'm clean again, been in the shower, had a lovely supper. I'm full and warm.

It's lovely living near Maxi. I can hear him bark at dogs passing, so I join in. I love being in his garden, it's huge. When a dog passes we both bark and I do about six circuits of the garden round the back of the bungalow, jump off the rockery, under the fir trees until I'm exhausted.

IT'S A DOG'S LIFE

Playing 'footie'

TO MAXI: Isn't it a nice coincidence that you
and I are alive at the same time? Sharing with a friend
makes twice as much fun.

EPILOGUE

My turn now. We believe we are Molly's second owners. Her previous owner had failing eyesight, so she put Molly with PAWS for rehoming. Although we had had four dogs, two cats and a few hamsters, none of this prepared me for life with Molly.

I remember feeling very excited at the thought of a new dog. My husband had seen her in the kennels; she was the one for us. We went to fetch her from the kennels and there, looking very expectant, stood this skinny terrier with very little hair. We talked to her and held her while she was chipped. She had been vaccinated. We had to sign a form to say that we would have her spayed after she had been living with us for three months.

When we fetched her home from the kennels they told us that she had an odd habit. What could that be? We were amused and relieved when they said she does a handstand when she pees. This has amused countless people over the years, especially children.

When we brought her home she was very quiet, and it was a week before she barked. Barking is a good sign; it means 'I am here and this is my territory'.

Not many weeks after Molly came to live with us I walked into our local pet store to buy food. There, displayed on a board, was a picture of Molly. It was an appeal: "Could you give this dog a home? She is in kennels and very unhappy with her situation." I was thrilled and proud to say that we had given Molly the home she needed. They gladly took the notice down while I was there.

When a dog has had a previous owner they can bring peculiar habits with them which are hard to change. After seven years Molly still gets very upset when we take off our spectacles or take our glasses cases out of the drawer. It must be something to do with her previous owner, who lost her eyesight while she had Molly.

Molly still has the funny habit of pushing into our legs while we're walking, and when we stop she will stand between our legs to tell us where she is. She will not follow us through a door unless you invite her; I guess she's been knocked or squashed previously.

Some of my animals have been fussy eaters. I always wanted a dog that would clear its dish of food in seconds. Molly has obliged with every meal since she crossed our doorstep, except when she has been ill. To slow her down, her first meal goes in a container with a hole in it. She has to push it around to get the meal out. She loves vegetables, so feeding her has been a pleasure; in fact I've never needed to wash her dish, she licks it so clean inside and out.

Do you remember the John Smith beer advert when the Jack Russell dog kept popping up above the bar as he jumped up? Molly brought that to every meal. She stood there jumping as high as she could to get our attention. She would also stand with her front feet on the back of the settee, from which she would watch us eating every mouthful. Talk about distracting – she really was a foodie. She couldn't get enough food in her to satisfy her boundless energy. I can't remember how we stopped it; probably by ignoring her, not feeding her from the table and giving her plenty of food to help her put on some weight.

Going from kennel life to living in a home was a big adjustment; she had been in kennels for four months. We took it one step at a time. We were strangers, and a dog doesn't love you overnight. We decided before she arrived that we wouldn't let her go upstairs. We had never made that rule with previous animals, but friends had a dog they didn't allow upstairs and we thought if they could do it, we could.

She had a lovely bed in the living room, but was having accidents in the kitchen. Slowly she started going outside for her toilet. We already had a cat flap which, at the beginning, she could get through as she was so skinny, but as she put on weight my husband had to make it bigger. Animals are basically very clean and a routine formed.

Three months down the line, she seemed settled. We had her spayed, and she was not well and felt very sorry for herself. Then the terrier spirit soon kicked in and it wasn't long before she was her mad self again. She was very happy with us. She loved playing on the beach. No matter how far we threw the ball she fetched it back to our feet – wonderful! We cannot take any credit for teaching her that. She's a very intelligent dog, and she probably worked it out for herself with her previous owner.

The big event in Moll's life and mine was meeting Sue and Maxi. The dogs have had a wonderful time together and so have Sue and I. Our lives have been greatly enriched and we've had so much fun together – long may it continue.

The duck pond has been a big part of Molly's life, and it's a lovely place to walk. She has however jumped in after the ducks many times. The ducks like to keep an eye on her and swim along with her. She once managed to get onto the island in the middle of the pond and the ducks flew off everywhere. She has been on the duck pond when it was frozen a few times. I am very torn about these adventures, as they are dangerous and there could have been catastrophic consequences. How much freedom do I give her to release her terrier instincts? We humans are the ones who have domesticated dogs, but I do not like restraining an animal too much.

Life is a dangerous business and it can't be lived to the full without embracing some of the risks.

An episode that gave me a lot to think about was when Molly was attacked by a swan. He could have killed her if she hadn't been as strong. Sue, Maxi, Molly and I were in the wood nearby when Molly heard the flapping of the bird's wings. She is so alert and quick she doesn't miss any sound. I think the swan episode really scared her; she has not been in the duck pond since.

Molly has loved Kenfig Pool as much as the duck pond. She has had so many adventures there. We are very fortunate to live near this pool, the largest freshwater lake in South Wales, named after a thriving town and castle which were engulfed by the dunes during violent storms in the 14th and 15th centuries. The castle keep is still visible rising up from the dunes.

She has chased coots out into the middle of the pool out of sight, while I stood on the bank wondering if I would ever see her again. Each time we visit we spend a few hours at the pool. She seems to disappear just when we are thinking of packing up for home. I am sure she knows the time; she swims into the rushes to hide. I have been in the rushes a few times and it's scary, you can get your feet tangled in the roots and it is easy to fall. We've bought a fishing net and a very long lead. If I can get close enough to her the fishing net goes over her head to stop her in her tracks. I put the long lead on her. She takes a long while to calm down as I have spoiled her fun.

We've had many adventures at Kenfig Pool. One day Molly spent a lot of time and energy swimming after a coot. When she got too close the coot would flap its wings and run on the water to put distance between them. Molly, swimming, would slowly catch up and off the coot would go again. Molly got so frustrated she began making noises, which sounded like shrieking. We believe Maxi, on the bank, thought she was in trouble, because the next time she shrieked he went into the water and swam out to her. When he got there he swam with her for a short while then came back to us. He must have thought she was OK. I don't know what he could have done if she had been in trouble. I thought it was wonderful of him to do this for her. Superman? Superdog!

Another adventure I would like to tell you about was the day we decided to walk round the other side of the pool for a change. It was all new territory for us and the dogs. The dunes were very overgrown and close to the water. The dogs loved it, as there were lots of new smells.

We could see across to the popular side of the pool where most people visit with their families for picnics. It seemed a bit too quiet and creepy where we were, with nobody around. We found an open spot near the water where there were lots of rushes. We sat and watched the dogs sniffing around, then they went into the water.

A couple came along with two Rottweilers, and they stopped to chat. They said they preferred this side of the pool as it was quieter. They saw Molly and Maxi in the water enjoying themselves, then went on their way. We had a restricted view of the pool and sat there enjoying the sunshine.

Then Maxi came out of the water and Sue took him for a walk. I sat enjoying the sunshine, but there was no sign of Molly anywhere. Sue eventually came back with Maxi and said they had enjoyed their exploring, but there was still no sign of Molly. We called and called her. We said to Maxi "Find Molly!" He usually finds her, but not this time.

After she had been missing for some time I thought I would have to go into the water and look for her. I had open sandals on and when I looked into the water I thought I couldn't go in there, as it was worse than the rushes over the other side. It was overgrown, uneven and quite deep, and it looked dangerous.

It was now getting late. I knew my husband would start

to wonder where we were, probably thinking that Molly was up to her tricks again. Sue and I had a 'conference', and the decision we came to was that Sue would drive home, taking Maxi, then call and put my husband in the picture. We thought he could come back with wellingtons for both of us to go in the water and find Molly. Off Sue went, while I sat on the grass in the failing light calling Molly now and again; nothing.

The couple with the Rottweilers came by on their way home and I told them what was happening. The three of us shouted 'Molly!' but to no avail. Off they went, wishing me all the best.

I began to feel alone and a bit scared, it was so quiet, with nobody around. I just sat on the grass and waited, and waited. Where are you Molly?

A short time later here comes the owner of the Rottweilers again. He said "I went to get in the car and drive off, but I couldn't. I thought of you sitting there on your own and decided to come back and go in the water, whatever." Off he went in his shorts and trainers, and the water was well up over his knees. After what seemed an age he came back holding Molly by her collar in one hand, with her legs dangling out of the water, holding his gentleman's bits up out of the water in his other hand. He'd found her in the rushes a few hundred yards from where we were sitting, enjoying herself swimming around.

I think I laughed and cried at the same time, at my knight in shining armour – well, shorts and trainers! I couldn't thank him enough. We set off back to the road and met Sue and my husband coming towards us armed with wellies. Molly was very pleased to see them and was wagging her tail, completely unaware of all the trouble she had caused. We all thanked the Rottweiler dad when we got to the cars and set off home, where Molly ate her supper and went to bed, shattered, until the following morning.

My stress levels have shot up during these episodes, while Molly has been oblivious, just doing terrier things.

In 2013 we decided to have a lump removed from Molly's leg. She had had it for well over a year. It started as a small soft lump, but it became harder and then bigger. Aspirations were done, and when the results came back we were told it was a tumour. She had her tumour removed on 8th February, and biopsies were done. The news was bad; it was a malignant histiocytic tumour. This is a fairly rare tumour, more common in big dogs, so Molly had been unlucky.

We felt so sad that this very healthy ten-year-old, with such a zest for life, would be taken from us prematurely. She could have had chemotherapy, but with only a 50/50 chance of success. The nearest clinic is in Somerset, and we would have had to travel there every three weeks for six months. We decided this was not a realistic option. It would have meant hours of travelling and the chemo could have made her feel very ill, plus she is not a good traveller. I weighed her regularly and checked her for lumps. Her scar took some time to heal; they removed muscle along with the tumour.

Her eyes have bothered her now and again. A course of drops or cream has usually reduced the redness, but this year (2013) they became persistently red and sore; the whites were bright red and she was closing them a lot. We had swabs done and they showed no signs of bugs in the cultures they had grown. Fortunately, after steroid and antibiotic drops, along with many weeks of soothing washes, her eyes cleared.

April 2013 was another bad month for Molly, as a bad diarrhoea and sickness bug was about. Both Molly and Maxi were ill and in fact, both of them came very near to being on a drip in hospital, they were so dehydrated. Happily they recovered.

Molly succumbed to another bout of diarrhoea in May. It was horrendous, haemorrhagic diarrhoea, and she was in so much pain. I began to wonder if these bouts were related to her illness. I spoke to the vet, who said they were not connected to the tumour; it was just bad luck having so many illnesses in such a short space of time. However since then she has been fit and strong and back to her old self, with no signs of her illness affecting her quality of life.

Do you remember me saying 'no upstairs' for Molly? Well, eight years on she has her own bedroom with a lovely bed. She loves sitting up there looking over the crescent of gardens. We can hear her talking away to herself, and if she sees something that needs sorting out she's like a rocket, down the stairs, through two doors with dog flaps. Being so ill after her surgery she didn't want to be separated from us, so we put a bed in our bedroom. Downstairs, we also put a soft duvet folded on the settee to ease her pain. She is now ruined, with beds everywhere.

The rest of the year has been good for Molly. She is maintaining her weight and luckily I haven't found more lumps. We have put our lives on hold to keep her happy for the rest of her life.

A year down the line from Molly's surgery, after a very healthy winter, we took her to the vet wanting to know how she was. After an examination and checking her notes the vet told us that Molly's tumour was so aggressive that if a single cell had escaped she would have been dead a long time ago. The vet did say she had removed the tumour whole, which meant taking away some of Molly's leg muscle as well. She obviously did a very good job, as no cells escaped, and she saved Molly's life with her skill. She gave Molly a clean bill of health – amazing and wonderful.

I felt very strange when we returned home; confused,

not happy. We had been waiting for Molly to die for a year. In that time we spoiled her in so many ways, thinking we would not be doing this again. I didn't fuss too much if she was muddy and came into the house. The carpets were going to be replaced and I planned to move the bedrooms around. Planning these things in my head kept my mind off Molly's plight. It was a very weird feeling, and it took me a few months to turn my brain around and accept that Molly was going to live. She has been so well since, and we are all very happy.

Famous last words! Everything seemed back on track and sorted. Then, out of the blue, a husky dog attacked Maxi. Being a placid dog, Maxi was very frightened. I saw the house where the dog and dog walker entered and crossed to speak to them, and the husky knocked me over and attacked Molly. She screamed, and was very scared.

When we got the dogs home, I had a big lump on my head and Molly was bleeding from her rib cage. We rang the dog warden and left it with him. The outcome was that the husky had to be put on a lead when it was out.

Molly had a bad night. She was so upset and breathless that I rang the vet, who suggested half a paracetamol and said we should watch her for an hour. The vet thought Molly was suffering from shock, but if she was still breathless in an hour it meant her lungs were probably punctured from the dog bites, which meant we would have to take her to the surgery. It was half past two in the morning, so we were very glad to see her calm down and go to sleep.

We took her to the vet in the morning, and she said the puncture wounds were very deep. She squirted water from a syringe into the wounds to see how deep they were. A course of antibiotics, and Molly soon recovered. Maxi had no outward wounds, but he was very quiet for a few days and didn't want to go out, especially without Molly.

When we started walking again they were both apprehensive of husky dogs. We did see the dog that had attacked them; Molly tried to run the other way and Maxi hid behind Sue. They were all on their leads, so there was no other incident. I'm sure it's taken a long time for them to forget what happened, and maybe they still haven't altogether. I myself suffered shingles afterwards, and I'm sure it was due to the stress caused by this episode.

Molly had a bad 2013, but the following year she was blooming. However poor Maxi was ill. We were on the beach one day when Maxi suddenly pulled up while running down to the sea. He was in pain, poor boy. It took us a long time to get him home. Luckily I had treats, which are essential when taking Molly out. It took all the treats to get him home. Molly however thought she should have some, jumping and performing, but we had to keep them for Maxi. Sue took him to the vet. They X-rayed his leg to find he had ruptured his cruciate ligament, which meant surgery and a very long, slow process back to walking. Molly sick-visited Maxi most days, and I'm sure she realized he was ill.

Just before Maxi had his injury, Sue was concerned that he was drinking a lot of water and panting. After many visits to the vet, he was diagnosed with Cushing's disease. We have eight pages of information regarding Cushing from the internet. It is a very complicated disease and difficult to understand. It is treatable with drugs, but finding the right dose is difficult, especially in the very warm weather, when most dogs would be panting anyway. He is now on medication for life. After four hard months for Sue and Maxi, he seems to be better.

I doubt if we will ever again go for our long walks down to Newton beach. When Molly and Maxi met they were three and one. Now they are twelve and nine. Maxi is older and wiser, Molly just older. She still does her own thing but keeps an eye on me now and again. Only once this year has she wandered across the front beach. I could see her in the distance and after about twenty minutes I thought 'here we go, let's go and find her'. I was putting my cushion in my knapsack when she came running up fast, ears down, tail down, looking scared. I like to think she panicked, having lost sight of me, though that may be wishful thinking on my part.

Molly does seem to have left the delinquent side of herself behind; some of her confidence has gone and she is now more loving. We still have a lot of fun. We have bought a paddling pool for her this year and she loves pushing her face into the water, making bubbles and then trying to burst them. She jumps in and out of the pool, and I don't catch her every time so my carpet is suffering. Good job it's clean water. The things we do and the price we pay! Molly has no idea how spoilt she is.

One day I found a lump behind Molly's front leg. What should we do? With her previous experience it was not something we could ignore. We had aspirations done and were so pleased to hear there were no cells, just a fatty cyst.

Today has been a wonderful day. After nearly five months of Maxi being ill and restricted in his exercise, we have gone to the beach. Maxi ran ahead over the flat rocks and into the sea for the first time this summer and happiness was written all over him. He was jumping and running, and if he could have, he would have said "WHOOPEE!" Molly ran with him and dug a hole in the sand to celebrate. We sat on the rocks in the sunshine with a very warm feeling inside and out. Let's hope they are both back to good health and will have more happy years together.

The supreme happiness in life is the conviction that we are loved.

Molly came to us as a skinny scrap of a dog with hardly any fur, and so quiet. She has blossomed into a gorgeous, mad terrier with a zest for life which is irrepressible. Her coat has grown and looks silver in the sunlight. Her white skin has darkened with age and she has grown eyebrows and ear hair. She is so strong that she has muscles like a wrestler. Her determination to do her own terrier things is another of her strengths.

I can't imagine life without Molly. My health has improved from all the fresh air and exercise I now have trying to use up all of Molly's beans each day. I hope her zest for life and her spirit are still with her for the unknown time we have left with this unique terrier, and her best friend Maxi.

This is Molly in a sentence: *I like to do things my way.*

FOOTNOTE

At the end of my book, I realise that from the love between our dogs I have gained a lovely friendship with Sue. The dogs are still so excited to see each other; Maxi puts his front leg over Molly, she lifts her face and he licks it. When she sees him coming she stops and tenses. Sometimes he knocks her over in his excitement, but she takes it in the name of love.

Sue and I look at each other and smile. It's a good start to our daily walk.